Tree-
HOUSE
COMIX
Proudly
Presents

AND CAT KID

WRITTEN AND ILLUSTRATED BY **DAV PILKEY**

AS GEORGE BEARD AND HAROLD HUTCHINS

WITH COLOR BY JOSE GARIBALDI

SCHOLASTIC

FOR A REAL HERO,
BILLY DIMICHELE

Published in the UK by Scholastic, 2019
1 London Bridge, London, SE1 9BG
Scholastic Ireland, 89E Lagan Road, Dublin Industrial Estate,
Glasnevin, Dublin, D11 HP5F

SCHOLASTIC and associated logos are trademarks and/or
registered trademarks of Scholastic Inc.

First published in the US by Scholastic Inc, 2017

Text and illustrations © Dav Pilkey, 2017

The right of Dav Pilkey to be identified
as the author and illustrator of this work has been asserted
by them under the Copyright, Designs and Patents Act 1988.

ISBN 978 1407 19212 3

A CIP catalogue record for this book is available from the British Library.

Printed in China
Paper made from wood grown in sustainable forests
and other controlled sources.

24

www.scholastic.co.uk

CHAPTERS

DOG MAN

Behind the Scenes

What up, Poochies? We're George and Harold!

Me too!

As you might remember, we're in **5**TH Grade now.

That means we're totally mature!

And deep, too, y'all!

AnyHoo, our new teacher has been making us read all of these old-timey books lately.

East of Eden

So we started making a brand-new Dog Man graphic novel!

It's a tale of good...

...a tale of evil...

...and a tale of **STUFF**!

DOG MAN and CAT KID

But before we begin, let's recap our story thus far...

One time, a cop and a Police dog...

... got hurt in an explosion!

In the hospital, the doctor gave them sad news.

BOO HOO!

Your head is dying, cop.

aw, man!

And your body is dying, dog!

whine whine

But then, the nurse Lady got a great idea!

Along the way, Dog Man has made some great friends...

Sarah Hatoff: World's greatest reporter

Zuzu: world's greatest Poodle

chief

Chief: World's greatest Chief

...And one terrible enemy.

Petey: World's evilest cat

I'LL GET YOU, DOG MAN--- IF IT'S THE LAST THING I DO!

In our Last story, Petey tried to make a clone of himself.

U clone 'em

But his clone was a kitten.

Things went from bad...

... to worse.

But one lucky night, all of that changed.

Li'L Petey found a new home...

...but can he
escape
his
destiny?

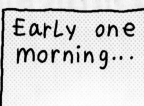

Early one morning...

CLANK CLANK

DOG man

CLANK

CLANK CLANK

CLANK CLANK

16

SLURP

Kiss
Kiss
Kiss
Kiss

Bye, Dog Man! Have fun at work!

Well, uh--- hello there, young man.

Hi, Papa.

28

CHAPTER 2

HOLLYWOOD HERO

by George and Harold

Meanwhile...

Uh... heh-heh...

COPS

Dog Man should be here any minute.

chief

Is he **ALWAYS** this late?

Yeah--- but, well, he's a maverick!

chief

He plays by his own rules...

Chief

...but he gets the job done!

COPS

30

32

Here ya go!

CRUSH

No! I can't work with him!

crumple crumple

He is an IDiOT!!!

* Italian for "hello." (Pronounced "chow.")

YoLay, this is ChieF.

HeLLo, DoLL!

And you must be DoG Man!

Yeah, but he's a Bum! He eats everything and he's always Late!

Ahh, but his heart is good, no?

Ciao, bello!**

** TransLation: Hello, handsome!

39

STEP 1.
First, place your left hand inside the dotted lines marked "Left hand here." Hold the book open FLAT!

STEP 2:
Grasp the right-hand page with your thumb and index finger (inside the dotted lines marked "Right Thumb Here").

STEP 3:
Now QUICKLY flip the right-hand page back and forth until the picture appears to be Animated.

(for extra fun, try adding your own sound-effects!)

Remember,

while you are flipping,
be sure you can see
the image on page 43
AND the image on page 45.

If you flip quickly,
the two pictures will
start to look like
one **ANimated** cartoon!

Don't forget to
add your own
sound-effects!

Left
hand here.

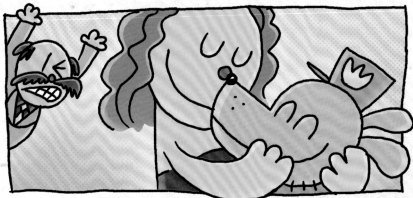

Right
Thumb
here.

Chapter 3

The Talk

Ice cream, Here we come!

Hey! where do you think **YOU're** going?

He's coming with us!

Sorry, kid!

Make him stay here!

But why?

Just make him stay here--- or **NO ICE CREAM!**

Wait here for me, 80-HD!

YOU'RE MY CLONE!

That means you and me are the **SAME!**

I'm evil, so you have to be evil, too!

You don't have any **CHOICE** in the matter!

But I wanna be **Perfect** Like Dog Man!

DOG MAN ISN'T Perfect! He's A GOODY-GOODY MILK-TOAST GUMDROP!!

He NEVER breaks ANY Laws! He NEVER has ANY FUN!

I don't wanna break any laws, either!

But--- YOU just **DID** break a Law!

I did?

Yep! I'm an escaped convict, and you promised to help me!

That's called "HARBORING A FUGITIVE."

CHapter 4

An Aching Kind of Growing

By George and Harold

Hi, I'm Sarah Hatoff, the world's greatest reporter.

Today is the 1st day of shooting for the new DoG Man movie...

...and the crowds are bursting with excitement!!!

Hooray

Let's meet some of the fans!

Oh, Look! It's Li'L PeteY!

And finally, it's comic superstar Scooter McRibs!

Hiya, Dummies! I'll be playing Petey the cat!

That guy doesn't look ANYTHING like me--- er, I mean, like PETEY!

Grrrrr

GASSY BEHEMOTH STUDIOS

And now, let's enter the studio...

...and go behind the scenes!!!

And check out our Pièce de résistance!*

* (French for: Supa Awesomest thingy)

EDEN MECHA-BOTS

It's **PHILLY THE GYRO!**

Nah—he's just another robot we built!

EDEN MECHA-B

I control 'em all with this complicated Remote!

EDEN

ON OFF

GOOD EVIL

WOW! Look at all this **STUFF!**

FiNALLY!!!

I can kick off these high heels...

ZiNG

ZONG

...dump this "old Lady" disguise...

FWOOSH

...And Start dressin' like my **True Self!**

RUB RUB

A filthy...

...Rotten...

...Ignominious...

And now, it's YOUR TURN!

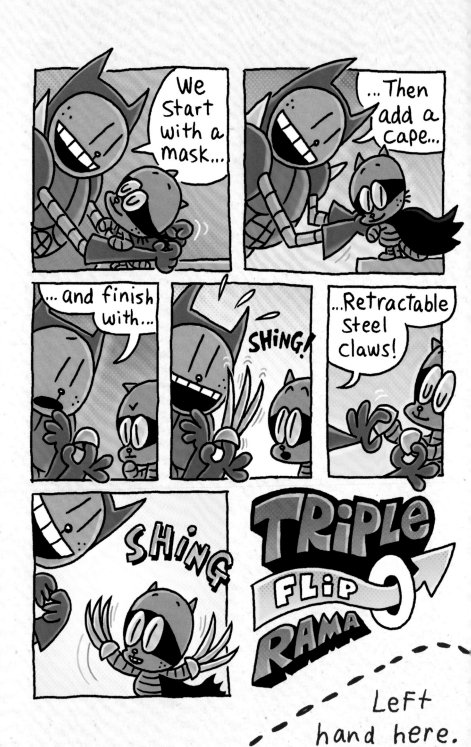

Left hand here.

Right
Thumb
here.

75

CHAPTER 5

You're supposed to be guarding **YOLAY CAPRESE!**

NOT Sleeping on the Set!

You made Ding-Dong Magoo trip and FALL down!

YEAH!

I have **HAD iT** with these **DOG-GONE DOG-Headed Cops** in this **DOG-GONE DOG-MAN Movie!**

DOG MAN, You're FiRED!

COSA SUCCEDE?*

*What's Going on ???

DOG Man has been **MESSiNG up** This movie **ALL DAY!**

FirST, he wrecked the big **ROMANCE Scene!**

Left hand here.

Right
Thumb
here.

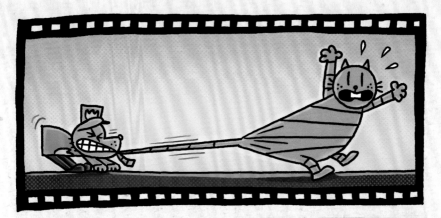

CUT!

89

Chapter 6

THE BARK KNIGHT RISES

COPS

I don't know what happened, Dog Man...

...but everything will be OK.

Go home and get some rest!

Tomorrow is another day!

Lick
Lick

97

But Then...

SCREEECH!

FLiP

K-SHONK!

KA-TUNK!

Wait here for me, 80-HD!

wait here for me, 80-HD!

Oh, hi Dog Man! How's it going?

RUFF!

Oh, NO!!! Is Li'l Petey missing again?

Coffee?

tea?

Hmmm... The first syllable is "Pee."

And the second syllable is "tea."

Pee-tea?

Peetea?

PETEY?

Are you telling me that Petey disguised himself as a NANNY?

And that he was mistakenly hired to babysit Li'L Petey?

And at this very moment, he may be planning something EVIL?

Or plotting an act of corruption that may tear at the very fabric of our society?

And even while we speak, Li'l Petey may be drawn into this foulness...

... causing him to doubt his own true nature, and career down a dark pathway toward a lifetime of nihilistic criminality?

IS **THAT** what you're saying?

OK, Dog Man...

...We're gonna go find Chief...

...You must find another way to get inside!!!

GASSY BEHEMOTH STUDIOS

GASSY
BEHEMOTH
STUDIOS

HEY!

POP

SO!!! You Thought you'd dig a tunnel into the Studio, huh?

Looks like you popped up in the WRONG SPOT!

What an IDIOT!

You're coming with Me!!!

Zip!

CHAPTER 7
A Buncha Stuff That Happened Next

PUPPY
ADVISORY
EXCITING CONTENT

I've finally figured out a plan to shut this movie **DOWN**!!!

C'mon, Kid!

Don't call me "kid." Call me "Cat Kid."

Why?

It's my Superhero name!

We're **NOT** Super **HEROES**!!! We're Super **VILLAINS**!

117

Meanwhile...

OK, PeopLe! We're about to shoot the big action scene!

Are the mini-motor scooters in place?

Yes, sir!

Is the Dogmobile gassed up?

Yep-er!

124

Let's put her back, ok?

NO! We're the **BAD GUYS!!!**

WE DO EVIL STUFF!

But Papa-

Look, the world is **NOT** A very Nice Place!!!

It's **Rotten---** It's **UNFAIR---** It's **HORRIBLE!**

And the only way to get ahead...

Check out our brand-new motto!!!

NOW...Do ya wanna have some REAL FUN???

Cut her down!

Use those steel claws of yours and slice the rope!

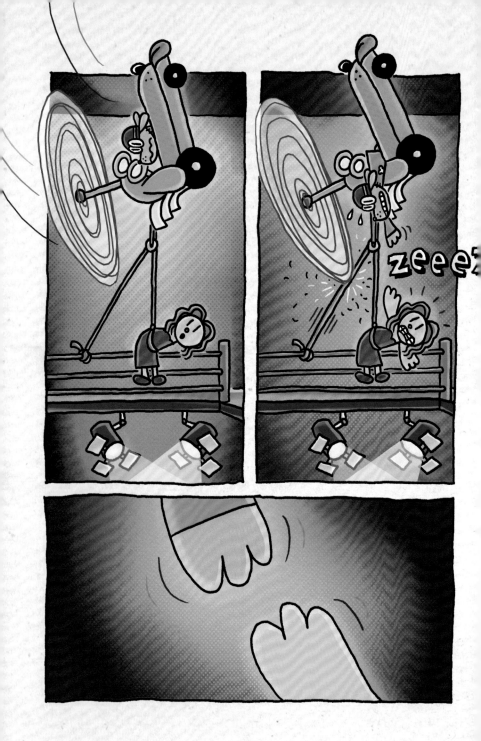

zeee?

SKRRRR

ZZEEEEEEE

ZMMMM

EXIT EXIT

Soon, the Mecha-Weenies began to Organize!

Listen up, bubs! We gotta DESTROY THIS CITY!

Oh, Look at the little cutie pies!!!

Right
Thumb
here.

BASTA!!!*

(*Enough!!)

I Think we're gonna have to fight these guys!

But you can't eat 'em, DOG Man!!!

They're **Robots!**

That's **RiGHT!** And you guys are **OUTNUMBERED** thirty to **Three!**

Right Thumb here.

And so...

Are you OK, boss?

DUHR--- ME GO Baby poo-poo Pee-pee!

So...

...Does anybody **ELSE** think I'm a dumb Superhero?

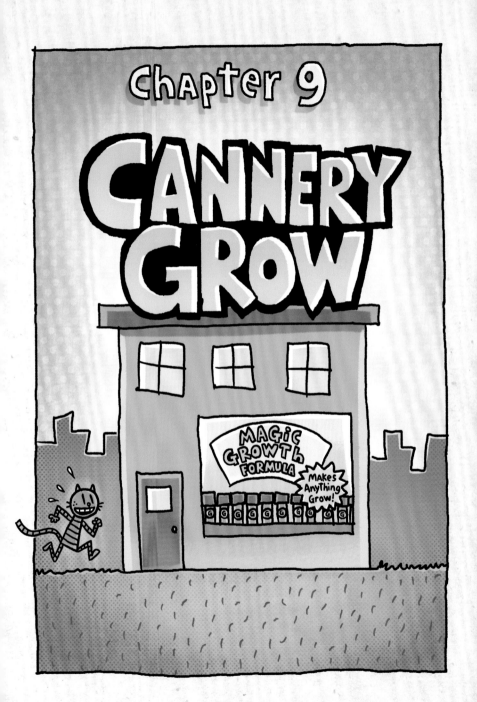

178

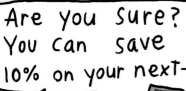

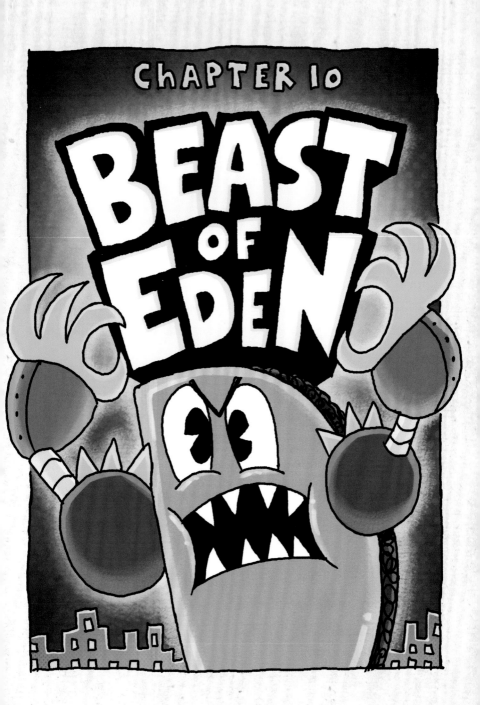

193

Right
Thumb
here.

201

205

207

They mean you don't have to obey...

...and there is no primary directive.

From now on, you can choose your own path.

You don't have to be my friend anymore.

You don't have to—

222

...You have the right to a mouse-shaped toy with a jingle bell inside...

IL Mio Eroe!*

* My Hero!!!

You were very brave today, bello mio!

Yeah...

...but I wasn't perfect.

And now that you don't have to be perfect...

... you can be good.

234

And so, the three friends worked and played together...

...until it was time for bed.

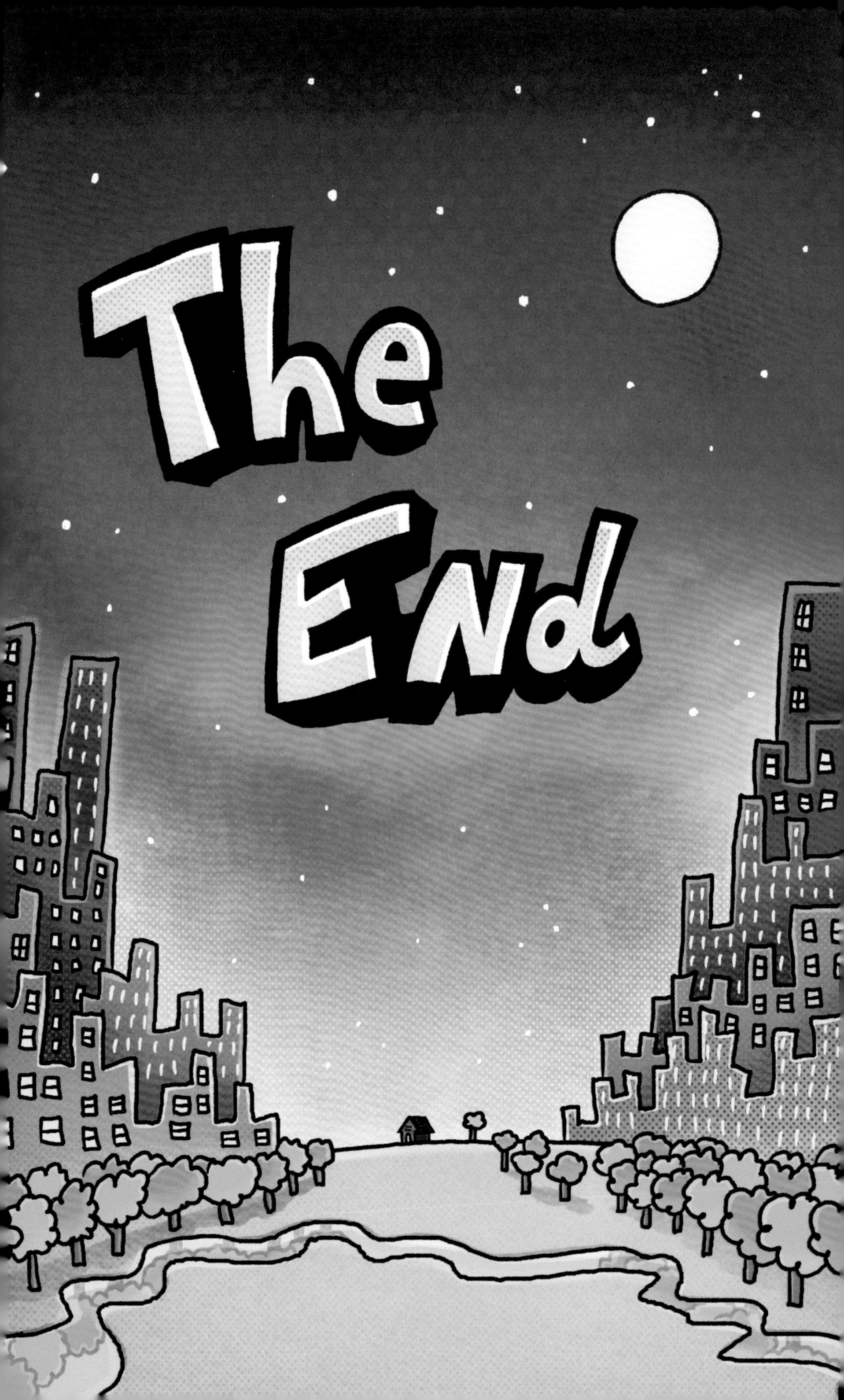
The End

BUT WAIT...

...if you thought our adventure was over...

YOU AIN'T READ NOThin' YET!

At this very moment, George and Harold are reading Another old-timey book...

... and getting a buncha New-Timey ideas!

So get ready for an epic tale...

...of depth, maturity, and intelligence.

Because a Brand-New Dog Man adventure is comin' your way!!!

FLIP FLOP FLIP FLOP FLIP

247

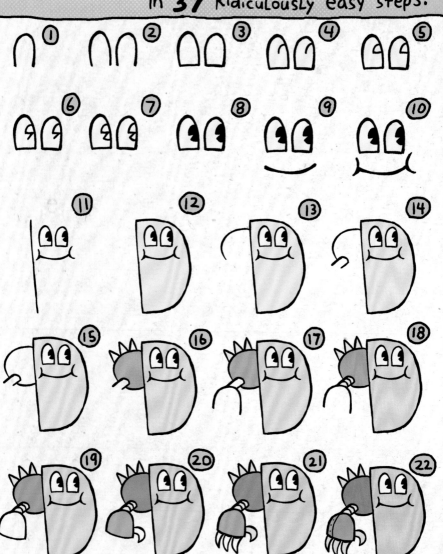

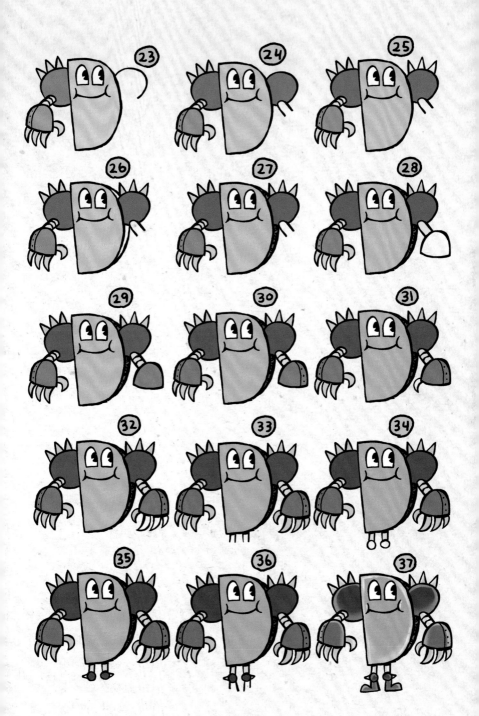

HOW 2 DRAW CAT KID

in **39** Ridiculously easy steps!

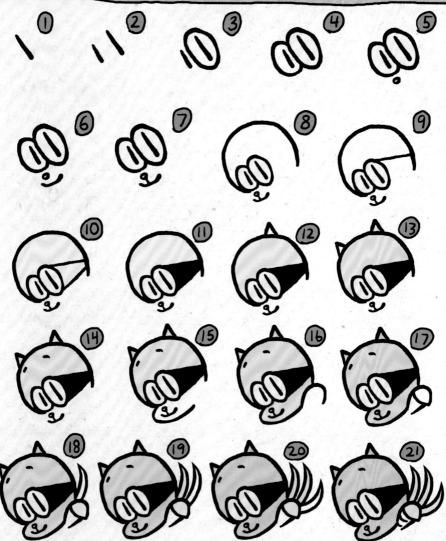

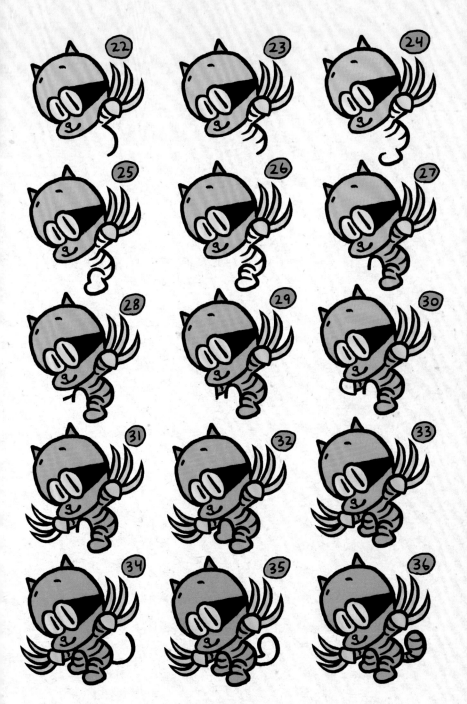

37 38 39

LEARN 2 DRAW MORE STUFF!

at SCHOLASTIC.COM and PILKEY.COM

NOTES

by George and Harold

★ The titles of chapters 9, 10, and 11 are parodies of the titles of Other books by John Steinbeck.

★ The words on pages 57 and 233 are direct Quotes from East of Eden by Steinbeck.

★ The Japanese words in Chapter 11 mean: Onigiri (rice balls), 100 yen (about a dollar).

★ "Timshel" is the Hebrew word for "Thou mayest."

ABOUT THE AUTHOR-ILLUSTRATOR

When Dav Pilkey was a kid, he suffered from ADHD, dyslexia, and behavioral problems. Dav was so disruptive in class that his teachers made him sit out in the hall every day. Luckily, Dav loved to draw and make up stories. He spent his time in the hallway creating his own original comic books.

In the second grade, Dav Pilkey created a comic book about a superhero named Captain Underpants. His teacher ripped it up and told him he couldn't spend the rest of his life making silly books.

Fortunately, Dav was not a very good listener.

ABOUT THE COLORIST

Jose Garibaldi grew up on the South Side of Chicago. As a kid, he was a daydreamer and a doodler, and now it's his full-time job to do both. Jose is a professional illustrator, painter, and cartoonist who has created work for Dark Horse Comics, Disney, Nickelodeon, MAD Magazine, and many more. He lives in Los Angeles, California, with his wife and their cats.